Badly Drawn Boy
The Hour Of Bewilder

Guitar Tablature Vocal

Published 2002

Edited - Anna Joyce
Folio Design - Dominic Brookman
Design & Artwork - Andy Votel
Photography - Rich Mulhearn & Mark Blower

© International Music Publications Ltd
Griffin House 161 Hammersmith Road London W6 8BS England

The Shining → 💡 🕯 CANDLE
Everybody's Stalking → ~~CAMERA~~ AXE
MEDICAL

MAN 1 —— Bewilder.
—— Fall in a River
—— Camping Next to Water
—— Stone on the Water
Another Pearl → SHELL
Body Rap → MACHINE
Once Around the Block → BUILDING BLOCK
This Song. → EP. 1.

2

Bewilderbeast → MEDICAL MAN 2.
Magic in the Air → NOSE
Cause A Rockslide
Pissing in the Wind → TOILET
Instrumental
Disillusion →
Say It Again → [o o] → → ☎
Epitaph - STAMP

CHRISTIAN.
BLACKBOARD BOOKS
RAYS
BINES
OFF
HEAD.
JESUS
3AMDOT
WOMEN
DENIM.
JAP CD CLOCK
PATTERN

LOTS OF
WED ROSES
MEDICAL -
RELIGION -
EP 1 -
GUITAR -
KEYBOARD -
BRUCE
WOODY
STAMP
KERPLUNK
DISCO BALL
SEA
MONKS
BIKE

The Shining

Words and Music by Damon Gough

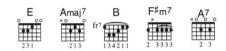

Andante ♩ = 93

Cello solo

Horn solo

Verse:

1. Faith   pours___ from   your   walls,   drown - ing___ your
(2.) this   slick___ fall - en   rift   came___ like___ a

Rhy. Fig. 1

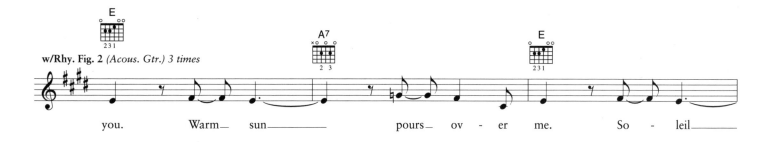

w/Rhy. Fig. 2 *(Acous. Gtr.) 3 times*

you. Warm sun pours ov - er me. So - leil

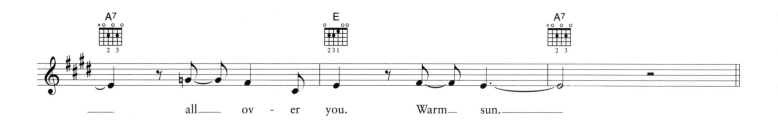

all ov - er you. Warm sun.

Interlude I:

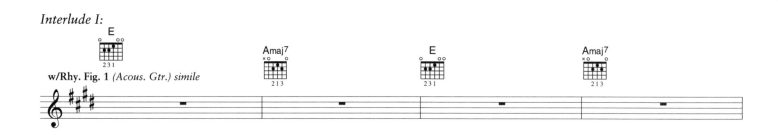

w/Rhy. Fig. 1 *(Acous. Gtr.) simile*

D.%. al Coda

2. Now

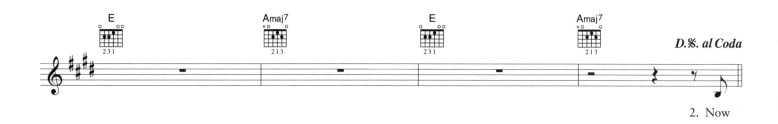

⊕ *Coda*

And sud - den - ly we're in love with ev - 'ry -

Acous. Gtr.

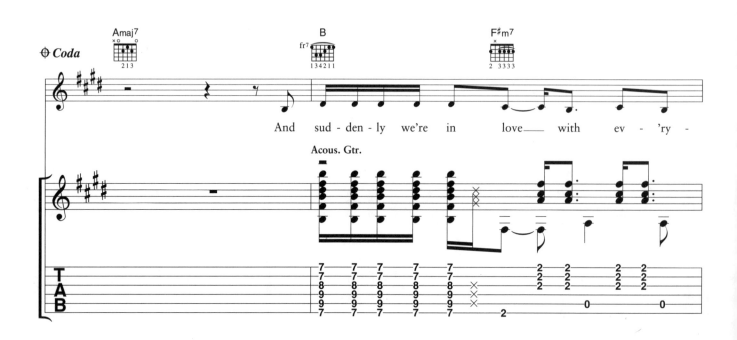

Everybody's Stalking

Words and Music by Damon Gough

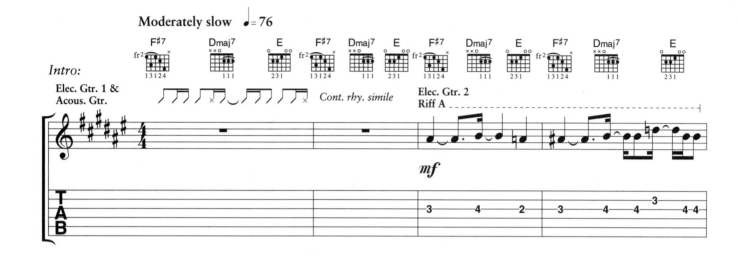

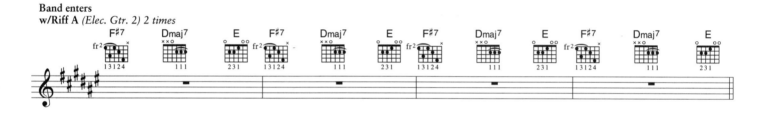

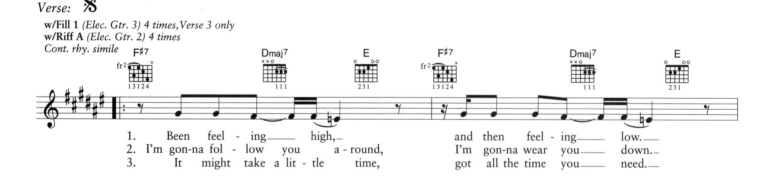

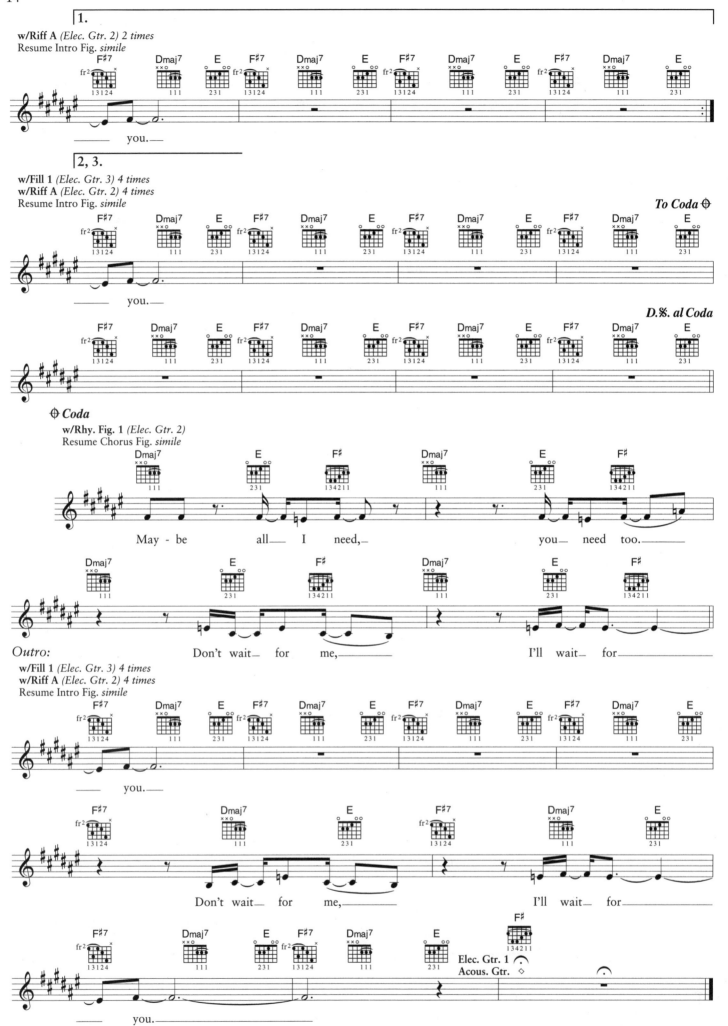

Bewilder.

Words and Music by Damon Gough

Fall in a River

Words and Music by Damon Gough

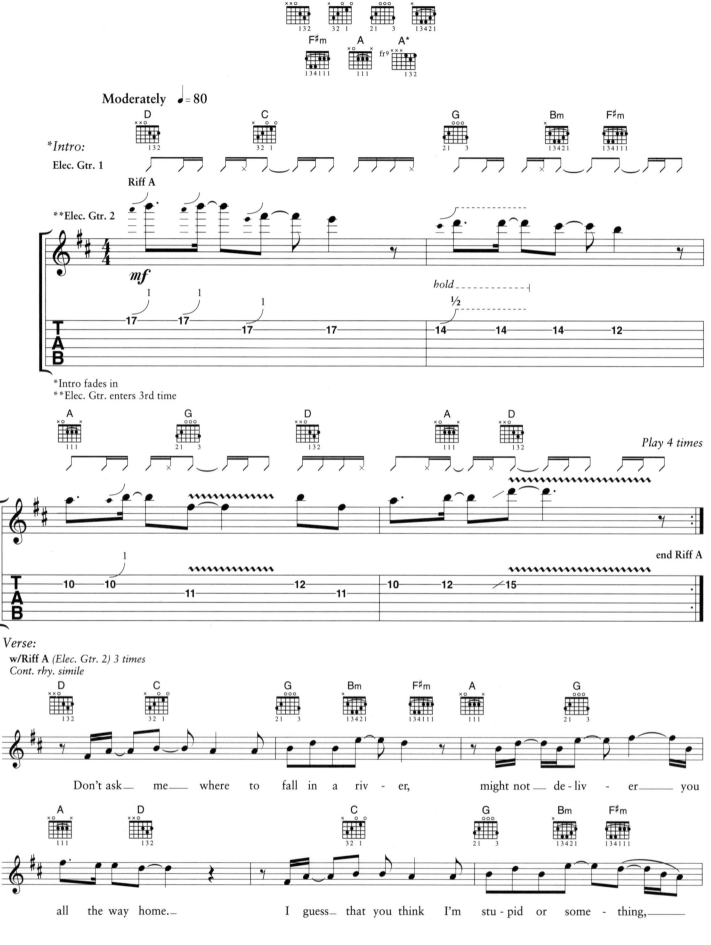

*Intro fades in
**Elec. Gtr. enters 3rd time

Don't ask— me— where to fall in a riv - er, might not— de - liv - er— you all the way home.— I guess— that you think I'm stu - pid or some - thing,——

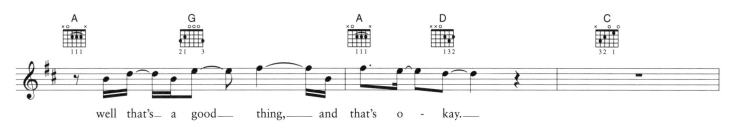

well that's— a good— thing,— and that's o - kay.—

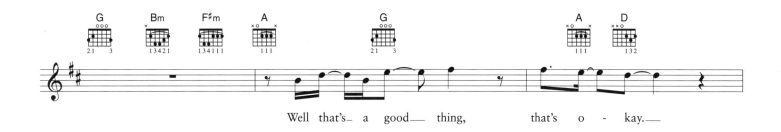

Well that's— a good— thing, that's o - kay.—

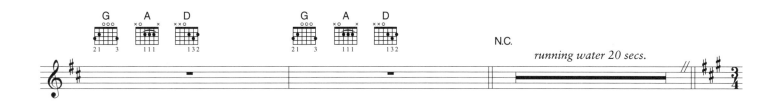

N.C.

running water 20 secs.

Outro:
Acous. Gtr.

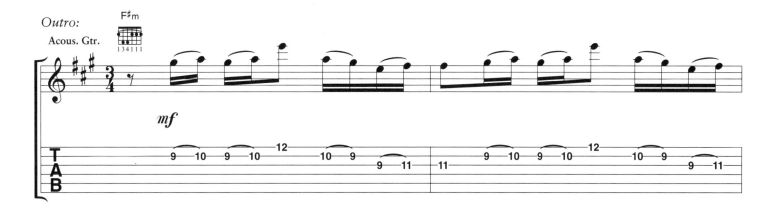

mf

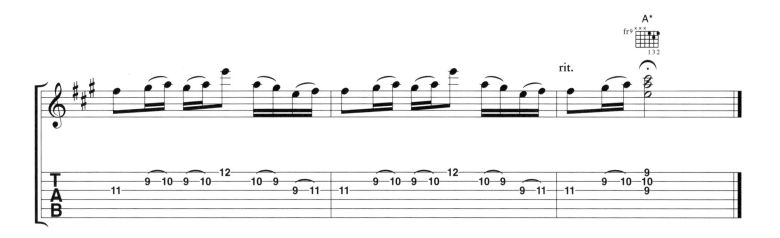

rit.

Camping Next to Water

Words and Music by Damon Gough

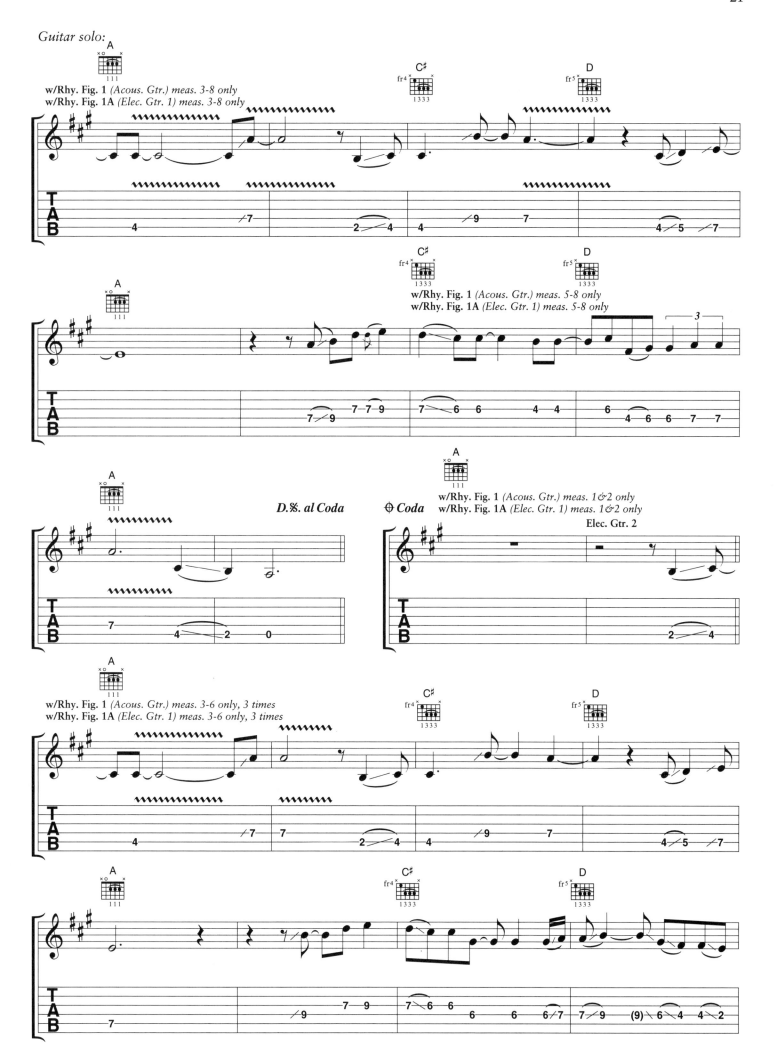

w/Rhy. Fig. 1 *(Acous. Gtr.) meas. 1-4 only*
w/Rhy. Fig. 1A *(Elec. Gtr. 1) meas. 1-4 only*

Stone on the Water

Words and Music by Damon Gough

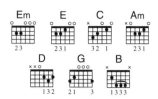

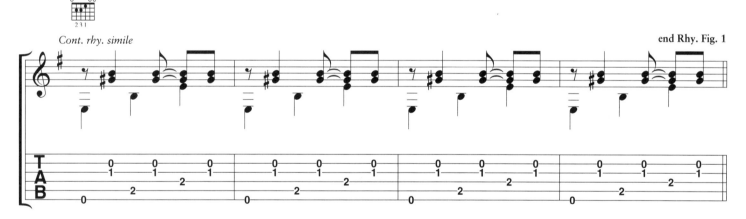

trace to lie per - ma - nent - ly.

Ooh.

Interlude:

Acous.
Gtr. 2

Acous. Gtr. 2 tacet

Acous. Gtr. 1

1.

N.C.

2.

Another Pearl

Words and Music by Damon Gough

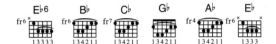

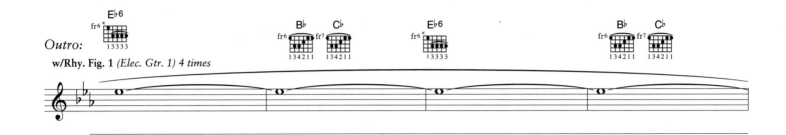

Outro:
w/Rhy. Fig. 1 *(Elec. Gtr. 1) 4 times*

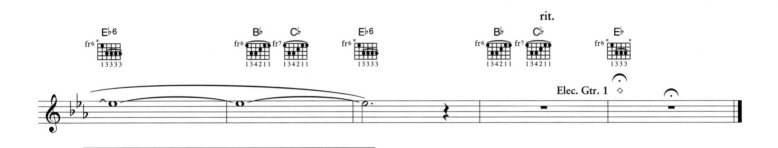

Verse 2:
Follow the gold leaf trail back where
We were young and didn't have a care.
Tracing the circles that we made,
I don't want to live life in the shade.
Will this be a desert or a beach?
Or a place to find the things we need.

Verse 3:
Now you and I make up perfect things,
Watch me trade my wheels for wings.
But don't ever use those wings to fly,
Just the eddence of a lullaby.
Now I am a giant grain of sand,
But I may be slipping through your hand.
Follow my colour coded world,
And watch me find another pearl.

Verse 4:
Let's walk to the sound of distant shells,
To a place where life would have no end.
You'd be the mother of my pearls,
If you follow me into my world.
Back to a place where we'd be free,
Where I'd love you and you'd love me.
This is the colour of my world,
Watch me find another pearl.

Body Rap

Words and Music by Damon Gough

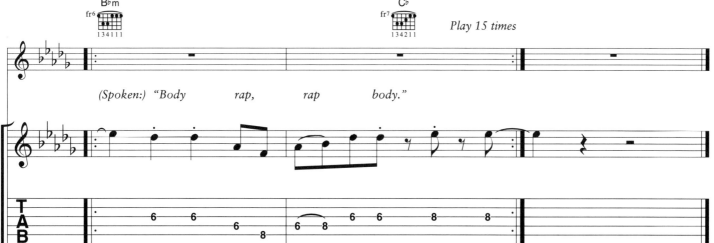

(Spoken:) "Body rap, rap body."

Once Around the Block

Words and Music by Damon Gough

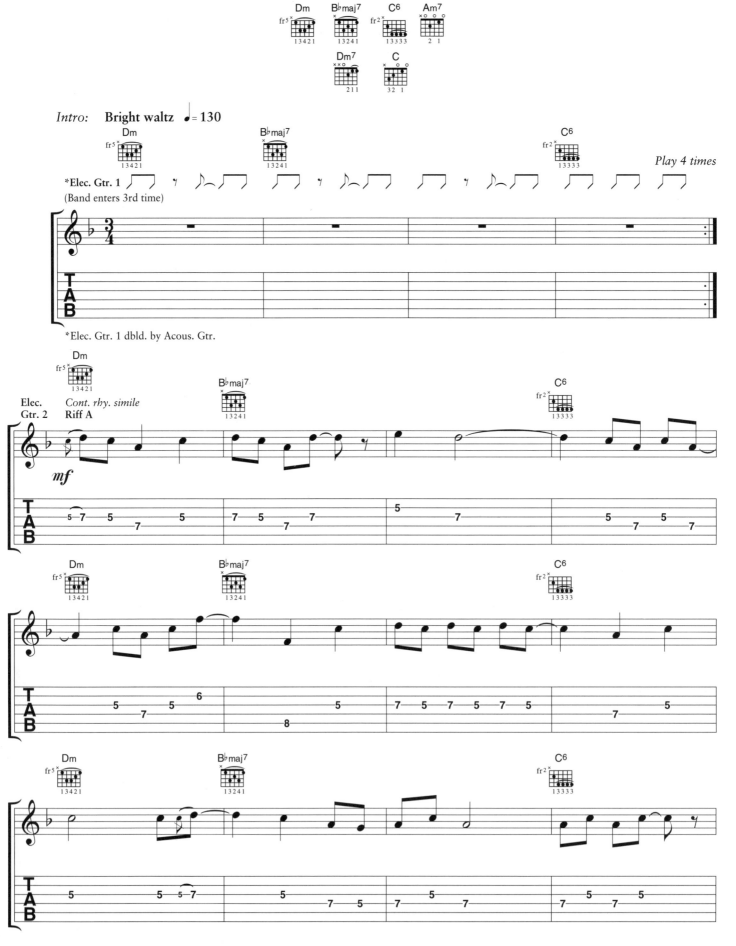

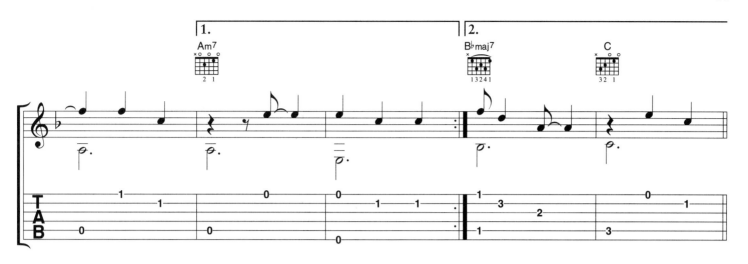

Mid-tro:

(w/ad lib. scat vocal)
Resume Verse Fig. simile

D.%. al Coda

⊕ *Coda*

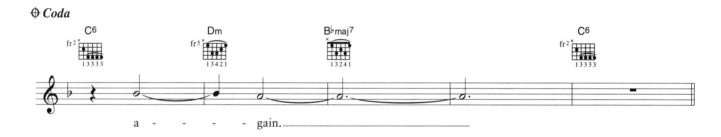

a - - - - gain.

Outro:

Repeat and fade

Verse 2:
You're feeling instead of being.
The more that I live on the inside,
There's nothing to give.
I'm infatuated by your moves,
I've got to search hard for your clues.

Verse 3:
I want to repair your desire.
And call it a gift that I stole
From just wanting to live.
Now I see the vision through your eyes,
Your innocence no longer fuels surprise.

Verse 4:
Trying to outrun your fear.
You're running to lose,
Heart on your sleeve and your sole
In your shoes.
Take a left, a sharp left and another left.
Meet me on the corner and we'll start
Again...

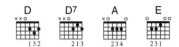

This Song.

Words and Music by Damon Gough

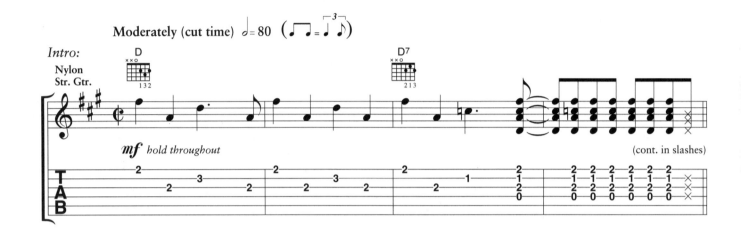

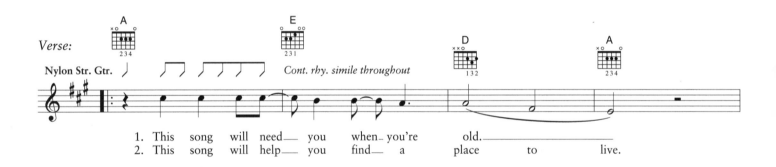

1. This song will need you when you're old.
2. This song will help you find a place to live.

This song will heat you when you're cold.
And teach you not to take but give.

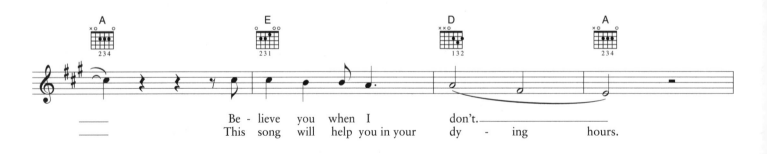

Be-lieve you when I don't.
This song will help you in your dy-ing hours.

Bewilderbeast

Words and Music by Damon Gough

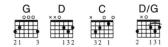

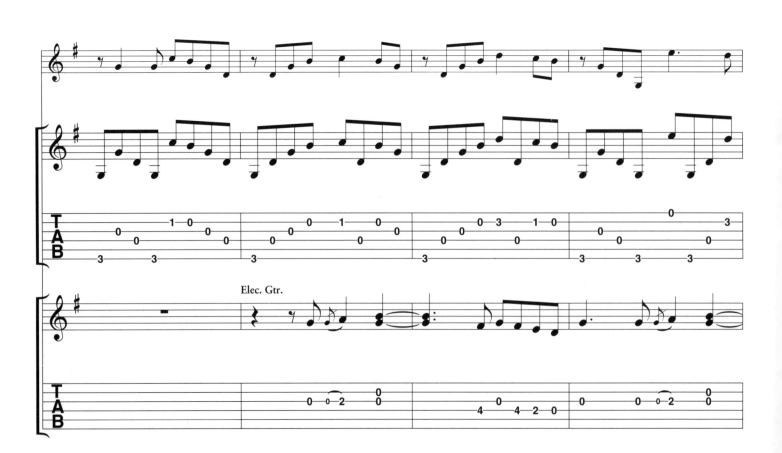

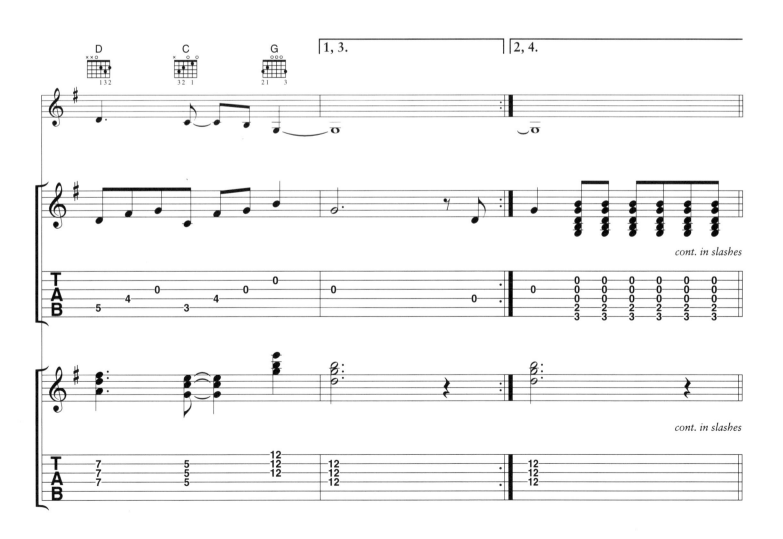

Cause A Rockslide

Words and Music by Damon Gough

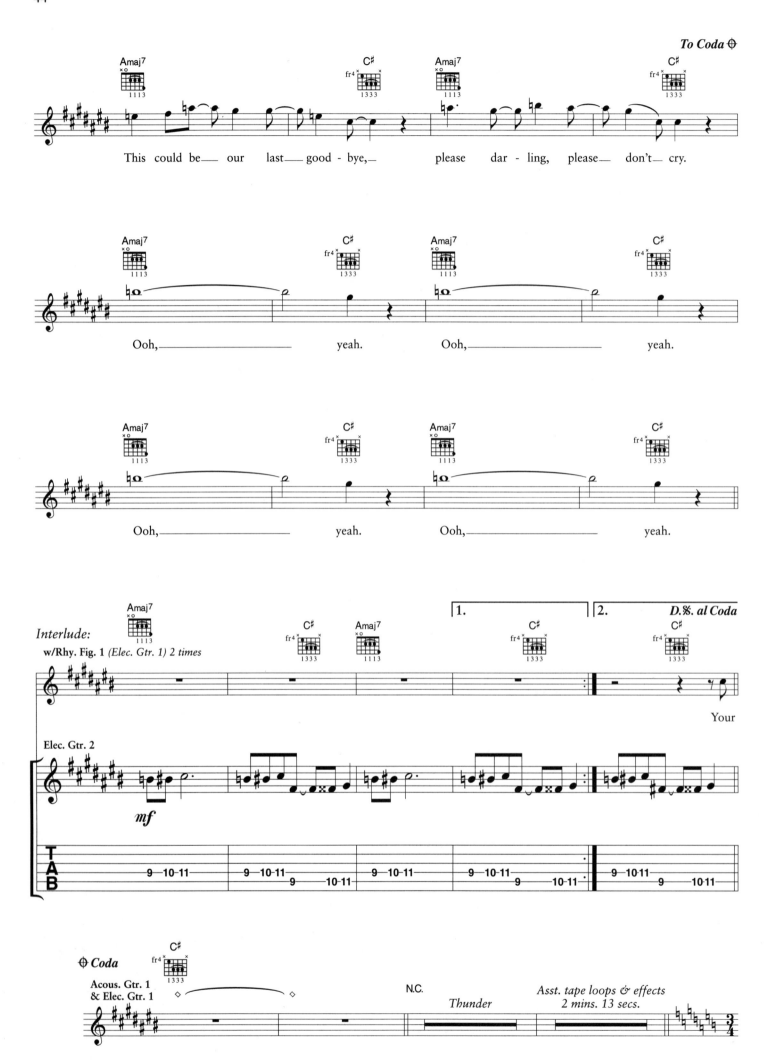

There goes an-oth - - - - er month, does - n't it fright-

- en you so.

Magic in the Air

Words and Music by Damon Gough

Pissing in the Wind

Words and Music by Damon Gough

Verse 3:

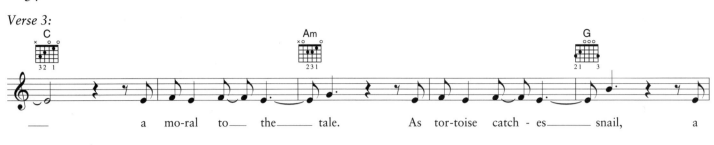

a mo-ral to—— the—— tale. As tor-toise catch-es——— snail, a

strong heart will—— pre - vail.—— It keeps on pump - ing,——

Chorus:

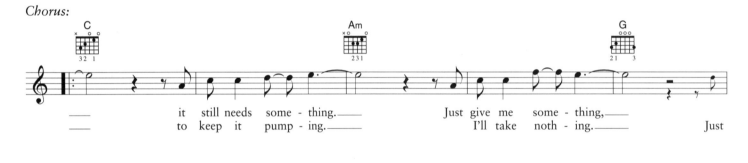

—— it still needs some - thing.——
—— to keep it pump - ing.——

Just give me some - thing,——
I'll take noth - ing.—— Just

1.

I'll take noth - ing.——
give me some - thing.——

2.

Just give it some - thing,— ——

Outro:

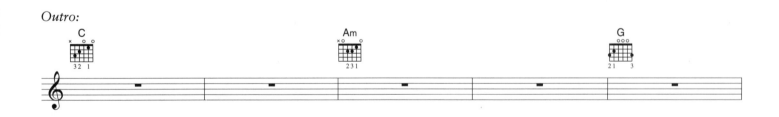

Blistered heart

Words and Music by Damon Gough

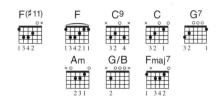

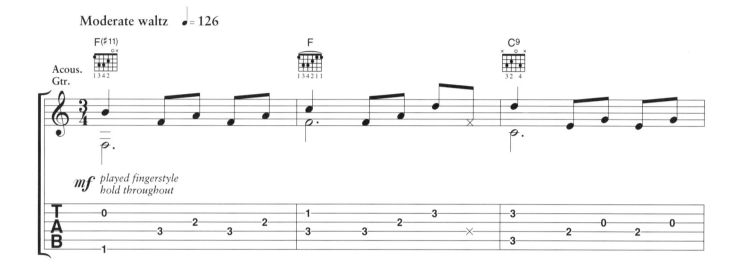

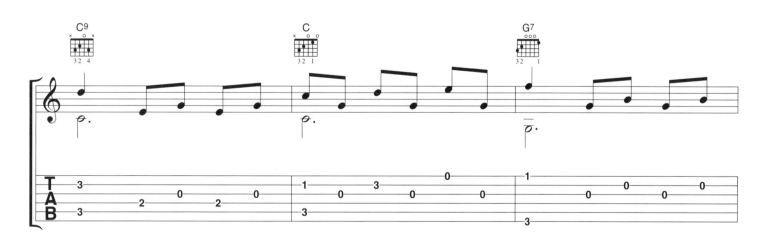

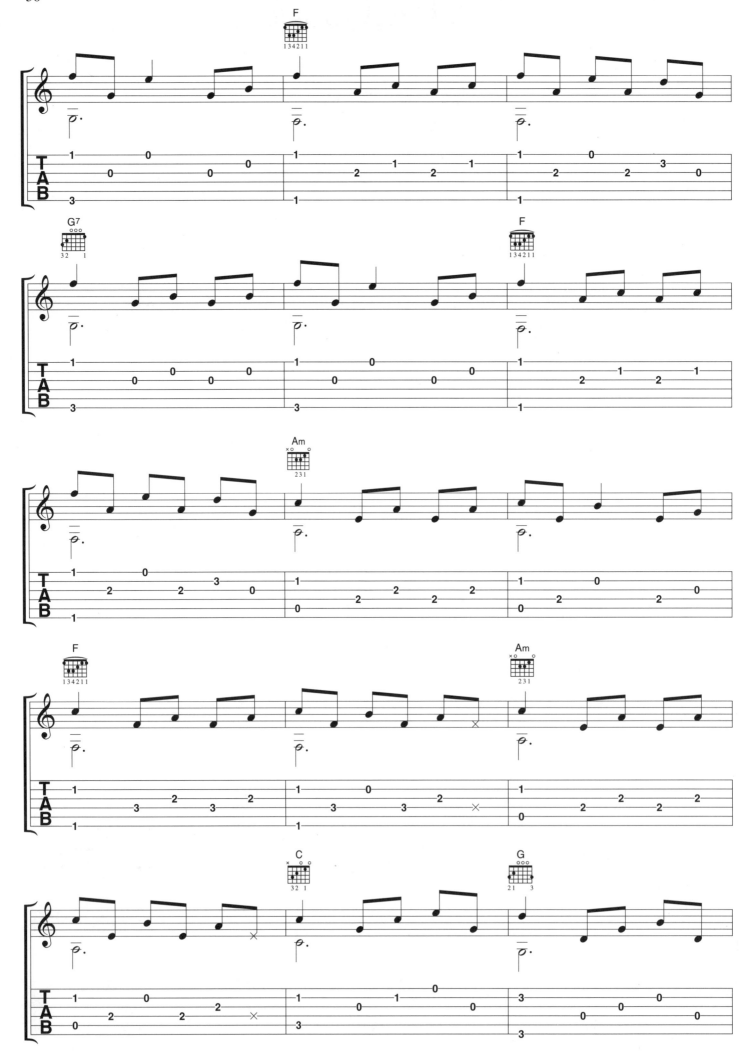

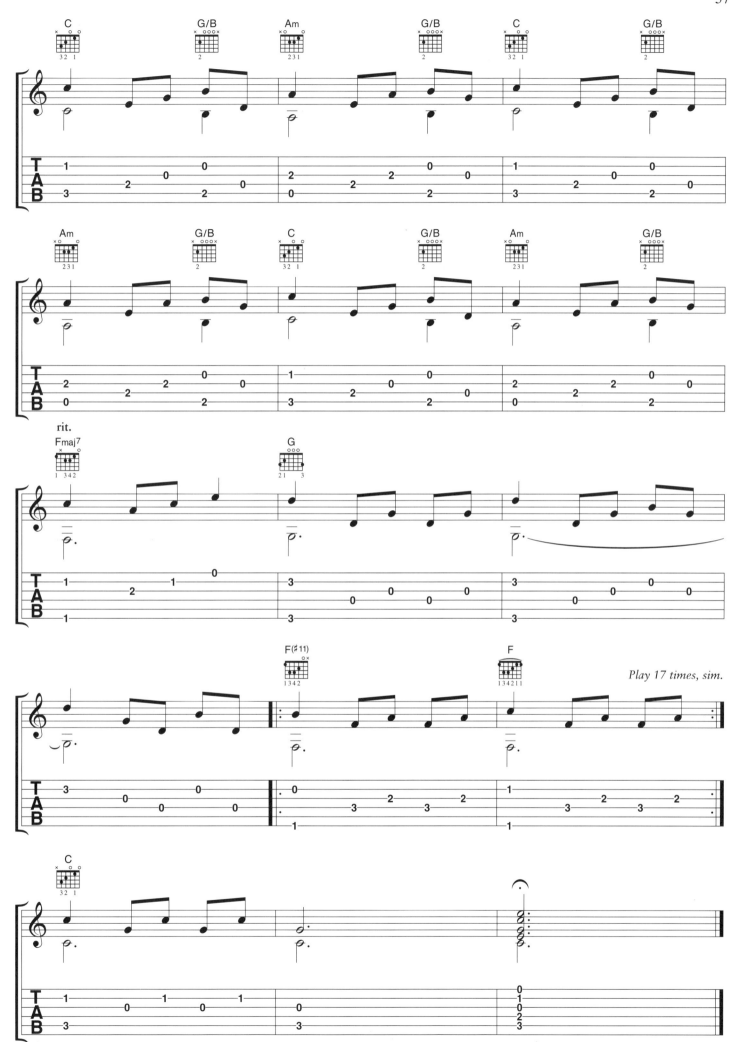

Disillusion

Words and Music by Damon Gough

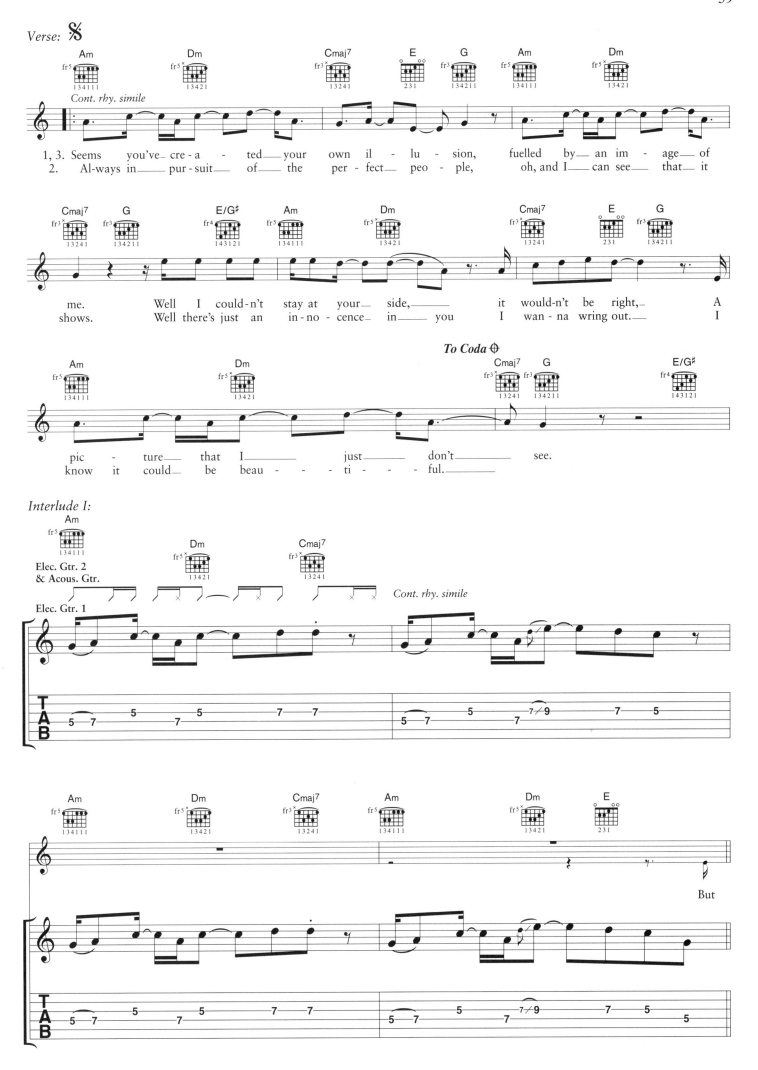

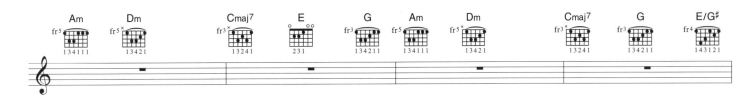

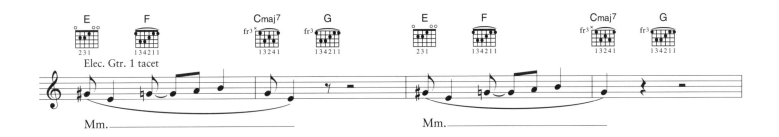

D.%. al Coda

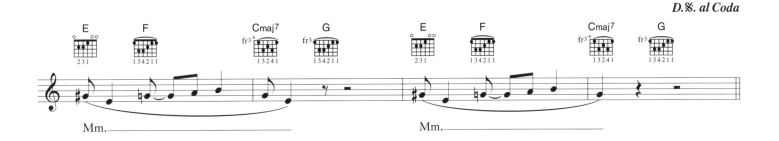

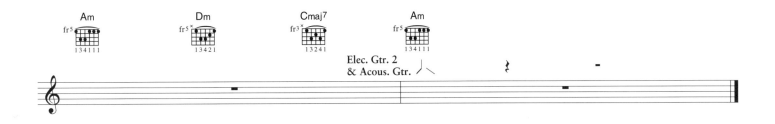

Say It Again

Words and Music by Damon Gough

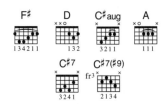

Moderately ♩ = 96

Intro:

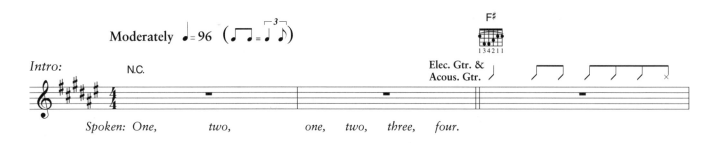

Spoken: One, two, one, two, three, four.

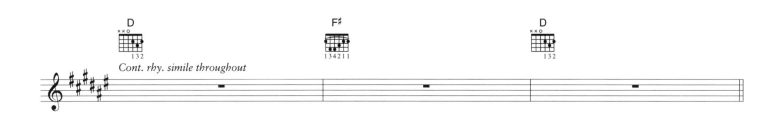

Cont. rhy. simile throughout

Verse: 𝄋

1. You squeeze the life___ right out of me,___ like sap-ping the juice___ of a bum-ble bee.___
(2, 3, 4 & 5 See additional lyrics)
(6. Instrumental)

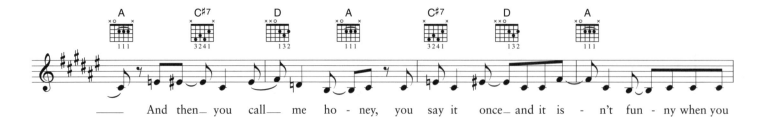

___ And then___ you call___ me ho-ney, you say it once___ and it is-n't fun-ny when you

To Coda ✛ |1, 2.

say it a-gain.___
(Yeah yeah___ yeah   yeah___ yeah   yeah___ yeah yeah.)   (Yeah yeah___ yeah   yeah___ yeah   yeah___ yeah yeah.)

yeah yeah— yeah——— yeah yeah— yeah.——) — yeah yeah— yeah.——)

Chorus:

——) Say it a - gain.————

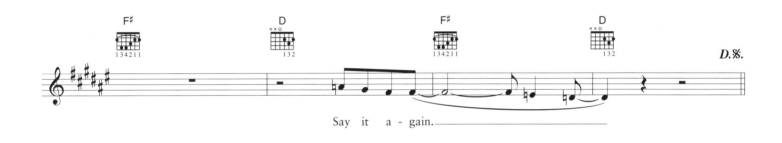

Say it a - gain.————

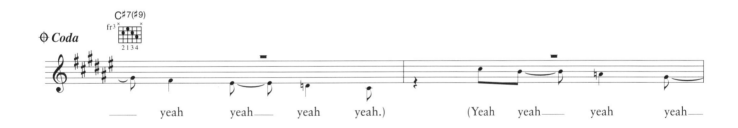

——— yeah yeah— yeah yeah.) (Yeah yeah— yeah yeah——

——— yeah yeah— yeah yeah.) (Yeah yeah— yeah yeah— yeah yeah— yeah. Say it a - gain.—

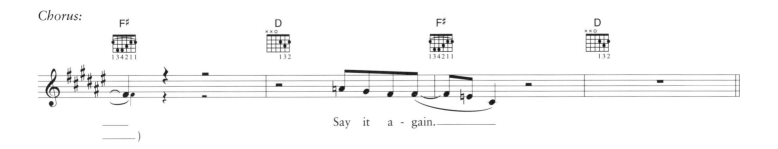

Chorus:

——) Say it a - gain.————

——)

Outro:

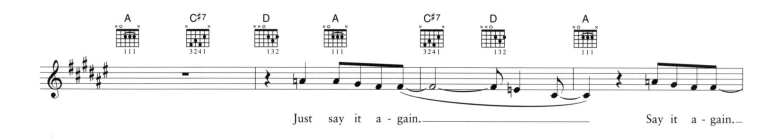

Just say it a - gain._____ Say it a - gain._

Repeat and fade

_____ (Yeah yeah_ yeah   yeah__ yeah   yeah_yeah yeah.)   (Yeah yeah_ yeah   yeah__ yeah   yeah_ yeah. __)   Just   say it a-gain.

Verse 2:
Now inside there's a style going on.
A head full of dreams, only room for one.
Now I know you can't live without me,
But I've no doubt that you'll never doubt me
Like you did before.

Verse 3:
And we're pumping out love into the sea.
I'm full bodied, I'm bursting with energy.
Cold blooded, your engines are running,
But where you're going I'm not coming
'Cause I'm happy here.

Verse 4:
Now we've found a rock steady beat.
Now all we need is a melody,
And words that mean something and nothing.
So people hear and sing along until they
Say it again.

Verse 5:
If there's trouble ahead don't be bothering me.
With no future I'll live on a memory.
Dried of thoughts but my nose is runny,
Say what you think but I know I'm funny.
I'll say it again.

Epitaph.

Words and Music by Damon Gough

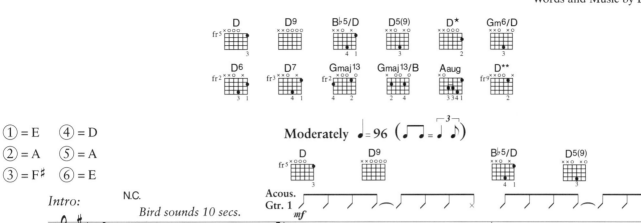

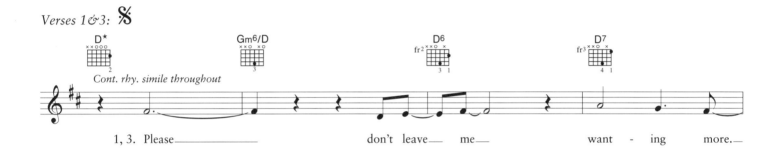

Intro:

N.C.
Bird sounds 10 secs.

Acous. Gtr. 1
mf

Play 4 times

Verses 1 & 3: %

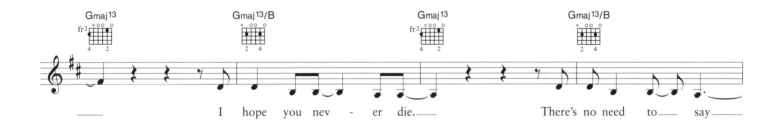

Cont. rhy. simile throughout

1, 3. Please don't leave me want-ing more.

I hope you nev-er die. There's no need to say

To Coda ⊕

why, just pro-mise that you'll try

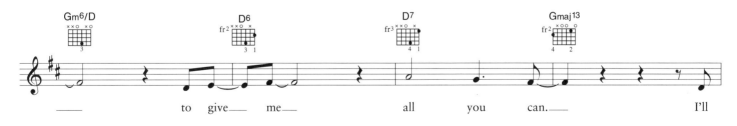

to give me all you can. I'll

66